The story of
a whale

Story by Roger Dunn

Illustrations by Peter Freeman

Macdonald Educational

Deep in the polar waters, winter is setting in.

The giant blue whales have fed here long enough. The time has come to leave.

This whale will soon give birth.
But her baby would die in the
icy seas.

She must journey to the warm
waters of the tropics, thousands
of miles away.

She travels with her family group, swimming for many weeks.

At last she arrives in the warm shallow waters of the breeding ground. Other females stay close by her as the birth begins.

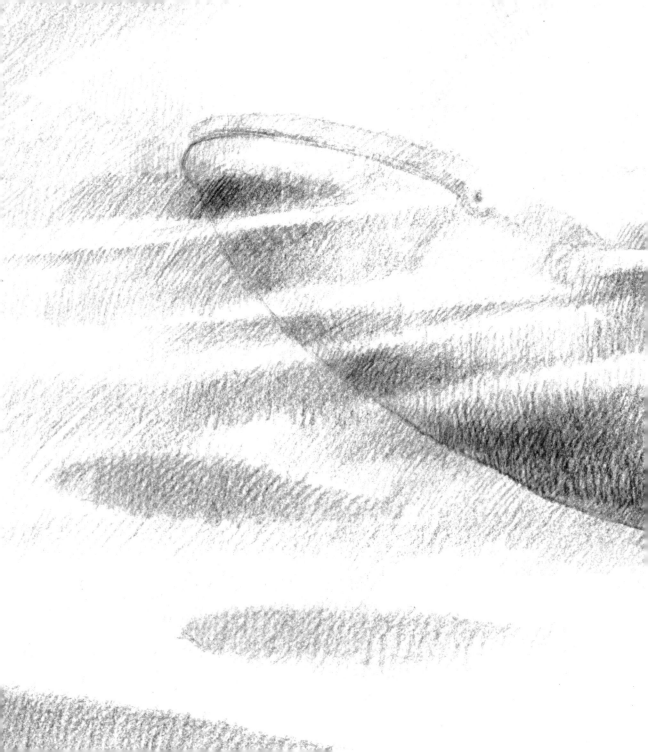

The calf starts to slip from her body.
He is tiny compared with his mother,
but still a giant. He weighs over
two tonnes.

As soon as he is born
she will cradle him with her flippers.

The other females help the mother
bring the calf quickly to the surface.

Without air at once he would die.
He takes his first breath through the
blow-hole in his head.

About forty times a day, the
young whale drinks from his mother.
She has nipples hidden deep on her sides.

Her milk is very rich, and he grows
about four kilograms every hour.

He feeds like this for seven months,
while she protects him and teaches him.

By the time he is fifteen months old,
the young whale is as big as his mother.

He swims with his mouth open, catching
plankton. Hairy plates grow from the roof
of his mouth. The tiny creatures stick to
them.

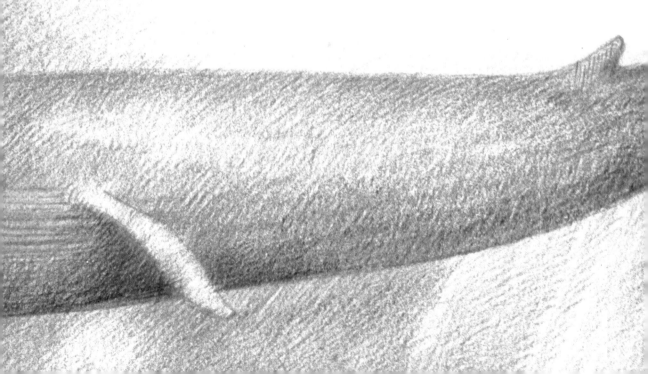

Every summer the group returns to the polar seas, where the feeding is best. Here they put on weight.

And it is here that the hunters went to catch blue whales, the biggest whales of them all.

Terror strikes! The whales
dive to the ocean depths.

But the young whale can hear his
mother's cries.

In a panic, he tries to help her.
Others join him.

They support her as long as they can.
But the water is turning red.

It is no use. In the end they
have to leave her.

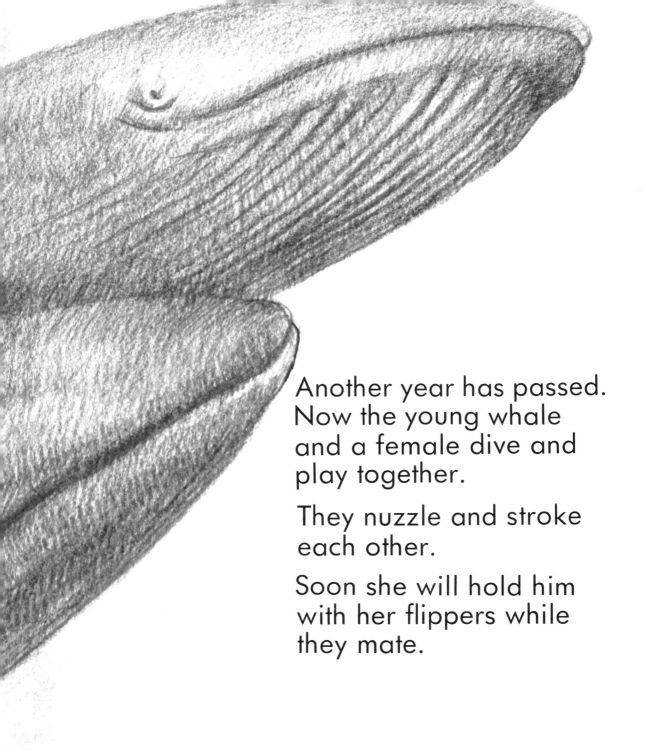

Another year has passed.
Now the young whale
and a female dive and
play together.

They nuzzle and stroke
each other.

Soon she will hold him
with her flippers while
they mate.

For a year, the two whales will swim and feed together.

Their baby will be born in the tropics half way across the world.